Thirty Paths to Peace

An Introduction

Thirty Paths To Peace was originally intended for local Yoga Tutors, Teachers and anyone working in the field promoting relaxation. I have taught Yoga for over 10 years and I found it difficult to source a little handbook which I could use in class, so I decided to write my own.

This is the second handbook in a companion set. Thirty basic simple visualisations, which have been tried and tested on my own students, therefore Thirty Paths is dedicated to all those who are continually seeking that still small voice within, that which is.

OM SHANTI.

Susan Johnson

December 2003

Thirty Paths to Peace

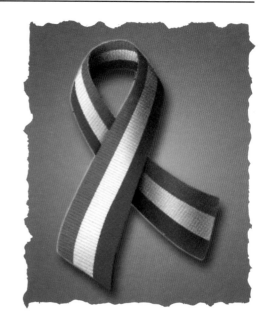

Written and devised by Susan Johnson

Designed by The Art Room
Some Photography by David Johnson

Printed in England by CP Offset Limited, Darlington.
Telephone 01325 462315
First printed and published December 2003

Published by Susan Johnson
© Susan Johnson 2003

Printed on ecologically friendly sustainable stock

Contents

Affirmations

An affirmation is a positive thought repeated as many times a day as you like, we repeat the positive thought three times. The idea is to change thought patterns from negative to positive and to allow one's mind to be influenced by a command. We use affirmations in Yoga practice. For example performing The Warrior we could use, I am Strong or during small relaxing interludes, we could use, I am peaceful. Before we commence Yoga Nidra we could use I surrender to this moment.

A Selection of Affirmations.

I am Peaceful.
I am Relaxed.
I am getting better every day.
I have all I need at this moment in time
I am still.
I am at ease.

Affirmations to Start Each Day.

Today I will stay calm.
Today I will stay in my centre.
Today I will honour all that I have.
Today I am grateful for life.
Today I feel safe and secure.

Relaxation Techniques

Allowing the Body to Let Go.

Allow the body to feel the mat you are lying on, allow yourself to feel supported by the floor, allow yourself to be supported by the earth. You are going on a relaxing journey but first you need to condition the body to enable it to recognise the difference between tension and relaxation. Sometimes we cannot let go of the body, we do not know how to, a good way is to allow the limbs to feel heavy, to purposely put some heaviness into them, to feel solid, and then to feel them moving away from you down into the floor, to encourage the body to feel dense, to feel so heavy we can no longer hold on, then allow yourself to let go.

Start to concentrate on the breath, and connect up to the rhythm, feel where you are breathing from, do you feel the abdomen slowly rising, do you feel the belly, are you breathing into the chest, do you feel the shoulders rise, allow the breath to gently raise the belly, to widen out the rib cage, to feel the openness spread into the chest, to open out the heart centre, feel the breath now spread into the shoulders, to widen them out, maybe you can feel the breath breathing the entire body. Remember the inhalation, the pause, the exhalation, the still point. You are now aware of the slowing down of the breath, you can feel the ease, the support of the floor, the body is breathing without any interference, it always will, all you need to do is just be. I am still, I am relaxed, I am.

Yoga Nidra

Yoga Nidra precedes visualisation. Before we start to imagine, the body must be totally relaxed. Begin the relaxation technique by allowing the body to totally let go.

Feel the body sinking into the mat, allow the shoulders to spread across the floor, move the head from side to side to release the neck, allow the head to let go. Imagine a cool blue light surrounding your body from the crown of the head to the tips of the toes, feel this light widening outwards, creating an aura of light around you. Feel it pulsating with life and energy, allow this light to be a healing light, if you feel in need of healing either mentally, emotionally, or physically allow this healing to take place whilst you relax.

Take the attention to the breath and allow the belly to slowly rise and fall with each breath, do not try and alter the breath in any way just witness the in and out, the flow, the slow coming and going, the evenness, the quiet rhythm. Allow the body to just be.

Now you are aware of melting down onto the floor, and you feel quite safe and secure,feel the colour blue soaking into the body, drenching all your cells with fresh life force, with energy, with balance, allow yourself to surrender to the healing.

Now take the attention to the feet, and allow the toes to spread and separate. Turn the toes inwards, flex and release, allow the instep to let go, the sole of the foot, the ankle, and feel the feet as solid and heavy, feel as though the feet are moving away from you, dense and heavy so heavy that you feel as though you are unable to move them. Allow the feet to relax and let go, feel them flopping out to the side. Allow the legs to release, the shins, the calfs, the knee and the kneecap, the thigh and the back of the thigh, allow the legs to release and let go, feel as though the legs are moving away from you solid, heavy and dense. Take the attention to the hands, to the back of the hand touching the floor, to the fingertips, the fingers and the palm of the hand, feel the softness in the palm of the hand, allow the lower arm to let go, the elbow, the upper arm, the whole of the arm releasing down, moving away.

Take the attention to the back and feel the vertebrae release from the base of the spine to the crown of the head visualise each vertebrae letting go and release onto the floor. Feel the whole of the back spread outwards, feel the back widen,at the same time feel the length, the stretch, the whole of the back spreading across the floor, and be aware of the amount of space the body takes up, the small amount of space.

Take the visualisation to the belly and be aware of the softness in the belly, the slow steady breath, the calm quiet coming and going of the breath, witness the rhythmn, the separation of the breath, the pause, and the still point, feel as if the whole body is breathing, that the breath is breathing the body.

Allow the abdomen to let go and feel the softness in the belly, allow the chest centre to open out and on each inhalation feel the division of the breath, allow this openness to create a space within the chest centre allowing you the freedom to breathe mentally and physically, allow this freedom to open out the heart centre creating a releasement, a feeling you may not have felt for a long time, allow this centre to be filled with peace.

Feel this openness now spreading to the throat to release the voice, to move around the neck, the back of the head, the crown of the head, the scalp, the space between the scalp and the skull, and even the hair on the head.

As you allow the face to let go and soften, the lower jaw slightly drops, feel the entire face release, the forehead, the eyes, the eyebrows, the eyelids relaxing in pools of darkness, the temples, the nose, the tip of the nose, the cheeks, the cheekbones, the upper lip and the lower lip, the jaw and the hinges of the jaw, the chin and even the ears and earlobes.

Feel the whole body release and sink down onto the floor all you are aware of is the steady breath, the rise and fall of the belly as the breath moves in and out, the stillness, the journey to visualisation.

Rotation of consciousness

Following relaxation the student follows the
voice, and visualises the object or scene.

Visualise.

Lying on a warm blanket.
An Indigo sky.
A moonlit night
Shooting stars.
Shadows crossing the moon.
Clusters of stars.
The Milky Way.
The moon lighting up the ocean
The gentle ripple of the waves.
The calm blue ocean.
The reflection of light
The stillness.
The tranquillity.
A lighthouse.
A sudden flash of light
A clear beam of light.
The Light beaming on the Ocean.
I am peaceful
I am still
I Am.

The Globes of Light

Lie still, warm, relaxed and at ease.
Imagine you have at your feet a bright blue globe of light, this is healing energy.
Visualise the strong blue vibrant colour, feel the colour radiating healing, feel the warmth, you may even feel a tingling sensation. Feel as though the blue healing light is now moving into the feet, relaxing the toes, into the legs, soothing the knees and into the thighs. Hold this image at your feet, a bright blue globe of light.

Imagine holding in the palm of each hand a bright blue globe of healing light, feel the warmth in the palms of the hands, the heaviness, feel the solid blue globe of light, feel as though your hands are pulsating with energy, you can feel the energy moving through your fingers into your wrists, into your arms, into the elbows, into the shoulders. Feel the weight in the hands how heavy they feel.

Now imagine at the crown of your head a globe of pure blue healing light. This globe of blue light is radiating stillness, calmness, coolness, tranquillity.
Now imagine a fine laser of blue light connecting to each globe of light and forming a circuit of energy and healing
Visualise a laser of light coming from the globe of light at the crown of the head to each hand.

Visualise a laser of light from the hands to the globe of light at the feet.

Feel the stillness in the body, feel the ease. The whole body is now embracing the healing light, you are being healed, you are being nurtured, you are being comforted, whatever you are in need of mentally or physically, at this moment in time, be assured, you are now receiving.

I give myself this time to relax, to be still, and to now receive.

OM SHANTI.

9

Five Minute Relaxation

Sometime during the practice in class, we come into a small relaxation period that lasts about five minutes; in these short relaxations we have an opportunity to practice breathing.

Lie in Shavasana, and allow the body to feel heavy, solid and dense, allow the earth to support you, feel as though you are sinking down into the floor, the body is supported, you are safe and all is well. Be conscious to the rhythm of the breath, where can you feel the movement, is it in the chest, belly, the shoulders can you feel the breath breathing the body, be aware of any sounds, you are alive, can you feel any bodily vibrations, make contact now to any sound, can you hear your breathing, tune into the sound of your breath, is your breathing short, hurried, or long and deep, how are you breathing, now be aware of the inhalation, the pause at the top of the breath, the exhalation, and the still point, start to count the breath, breathe into four, pause, and breathe out to four, pause, breathe into five, pause, breathe out to five, pause, this is a simple breathing technique which can be strengthened by lengthening the breath and holding the pause for longer but for small relaxations acknowledgement of the pause is sufficient.

Five Minute Relaxation

Lie in Shavasana, and feel the weight of the body on the floor, feel comfortable, at ease and relaxed, allow the shoulders to spread, the lower back to open, feel the length in the spine how much space you are taking up on the floor, find your calm centre, and start to be aware of the flow of your breath, breathe easy, feel the breath breathing the body.

Take the attention to the feet and visualise the feet as empty, hollow, full of space, light, let them rest for a while, be conscious of the legs and feel the legs as hollow and empty, feel space in the legs around the kneecaps, and let them rest on the floor.

Feel the hands resting on the floor how soft they feel, fingers slightly curled, be aware of the hands as empty and hollow feel the arms hollow and empty, relaxing onto the floor, connect with the breath, be aware of the softness in the belly how relaxed it feels, empty, hollow full of space, allowing the breath to flow with quiet even rhythm, take your attention to the heart centre, and feel a hollow empty chamber, all this space is allowing you to breathe fully, openly, allowing the lungs to fill with new prana, this prana can now move unimpeded around the body because it is empty, and hollow.

Visualise the prana filling the legs returning them to normal weight, the hands, the arms, prana is filling the entire body, moving around the abdomen, the chest, filling you with a complete new supply of energy.

You now feel your weight on the floor, fully returned to your natural self.

Nadi Sodhana Pranayama

Alternate Nostril Breathing with the
Emerald Mist

Alternate Nostril Breathing consists of deep
controlled breathing through each nostril to
purify the nerves. .It is usually practiced
following the Asana or just before
relaxation. You can do this practice back to
back with a partner which adds to the
energy experience or lean against the wall if
the back is tired, the most important
request is to keep the spine erect but
relaxed, to allow for the free flow of prana
to move upwards, be comfortable warm
and at ease, be prepared to sit for at least
10 minutes.

Concentrate on the breath, how is the
breath flowing, is it fast, irregular or slow
and calm, take a few moments to adjust
the body and allow the shoulders to
release, the belly to feel soft and relaxed,
the chest to open out, to allow space to
breathe, feel in that opening out a release,
a contentment, just to be where you are at
this moment in time, I am still, I am still.
The breathing is slowing down, releasing,
relaxing, you are allowing the breath to
breathe the body, and you are just
witnessing the calm flow, in and out, open
and close, expand and release, you are
relaxed but alert.

To bring more awareness into the practice,
visualise the nose as a triangle and the
breath as emerald green mist.

Now be aware of the breath coming in
through the nostrils, through both nostrils ,

feel the breath as it touches the tip of the
nose, be aware of the flow, is the breath
balanced or does one side feel more free
than the other, is the breath warm or cool,
what do you experience with the flow. Draw
in the breath and visualise the meeting of
the breath at the top of the triangle the
eyebrow centre and imagine here a uniting
of the breath a joining of prana. Practice
this breathing for a few minutes.

In Yoga we say the left nostril is Ida the
moon and the right nostril is Pingala the
Sun. Ida is cool; Pingala is warm, Positive
and Negative, Yin and Yan.

Now using the thumb and third finger close
the nostrils. The little finger and the ring
finger stay tucked into the palm of the
hand. The first finger stays on the eyebrow
centre, the Third Eye.

Breathe into your right nostril keeping the
left nostril closed, close the right nostril and
hold the breath as in pause, open the left
nostril and breathe out. Pause. Breathe in
through the left nostril; close both nostrils
and hold the pause, once again exhale
through the right nostril. This completes
one round.

Now bring the awareness into the practice,
Visualise the nose as a Triangle, the apex at
the bridge of the nose, the breath touching
the third eye as it moves through the apex
of the triangle and unites the prana, and
the colour emerald green as the breath.
See the colour as a fine swirl of mist.

Start the visualisation by seeing the breath as a stream of misty emerald green light, as you breathe in you feel the coolness of the colour emerald green, it touches the lips, the tip of the nose, moves up the nostrils, touching the top of the triangle it unites in the brow centre, and flows down into the chest.

The fresh prana brings new life-force, and you can feel the renewal as the breath moves deep into the chest centre, feel the misty emerald light finding it's way into the heart chamber where it moves into every particle, opening out this centre,

activating energy, creating balance and harmony, swirling and moving, spiralling and descending, circling around and around this emerald green mist dissolves negative ions, discharges positive ions, removes any blockages and creates channels for prana .

Move into the final round and bring into the practice the healing emerald green mist moving through the triangle to connect with the Third Eye, the rhythm of the breath, remember the pause at the top of the breath, the still point, and the calm centre.

Ujjayi Breathe in Blue

Ujjayi is known as the Victorious Breath. It is a Pranayama Technique and is simple to follow. The concentration is on the sound at the back of the throat, similar to a light snoring vibration. The throat centre is the Vishuddha Chakra it is connected to sound and vibration. If this centre is free and open we have good communication skills, we can walk our talk, speak our mind and express ourselves, if we have a blockage here, we are unable to express ourselves, always wishing we had said something different, we can feel insecure with people or we suffer from physical problems like sore throats or thyroid, some of these problems cannot be avoided if they are hereditary. The colour for the throat area is Blue. You can do this breathing exercise in a relaxation position or in sitting meditation.

Sit in the correct position with the back straight to allow for the free flow of prana Breathe out fully, breathe in, and draw the abdomen in slightly, fill the lungs with air and feel it open out your chest, expanding and widening. As you breathe in the air passing over the palate should make the sound sa hold for two or three seconds and release the breath, making the sound ha, keep the abdomen firm not tight. Wait a few seconds and repeat with the colour blue.

Breathing in blue

Visualise the throat area and surround it with the colour deep blue, feel it bathing into this area, deepening and widening around the throat and neck, imagine the thyroid gland and isolate it, imagine a beam of light going into the thyroid gland, supporting, stimulating, and resting it.

Now as you take an in breath visualise yourself inhaling the colour blue like a fine thread of light feel it coming into the nostrils as cool blue, be aware of both sides of the nostrils. Feel it going down the back of the throat to the sound of sa, hear the sound, the vibration, hold the breath momentarily, be aware of the pause, and let the breath go with the sound of ha. Visualise the exhalation as pale blue, the nourishment of the prana has been absorbed and you are now releasing the residue of the colour. Repeat this breathing technique for at least 10 rounds. As you increase the exercise the breathing becomes longer and more steady. The sound increases and the whole practice becomes a Mantra.

Trataka

Concentrated Gazing

Trataka develops concentration skills which can enhance all Yoga practice.10 minutes is sufficient in the general Yoga class.
Requirements: **A large lit candle.**

Sit in a Meditation Asana position with the spine comfortable and straight. Hands in Mudra, or in the lap, whichever feels comfortable to you. The room is dark. You can lean against the wall if your back is tired. Have a warm blanket or shawl around the shoulders and feel comfortable. Tune into the breathing be aware of the breathing, the inhalation, the pause, the exhalation and the still point. Feel the breath slowing down, relaxing, releasing, be aware of the shoulders, let the shoulders go without slumping, feel the hands relaxed, and just be aware of the rise and fall of the body. Feel which part of the body is moving, the belly, the chest, the shoulders, allow the shoulders to widen feel the chest open, create some space in the heart centre allowing the body to breathe mentally and physically, feel more relaxed at ease.

Now close the eyes and be conscious of looking into the eyebrow centre the third eye, open the eyes and between lowered lids, gaze directly into the candle flame and observe, look at the size of the flame how it lengthens and shortens, the flicker, the shape, does it curve outwards, Now look at the colour, the aura around the flame, maybe a double aura, the wick, the darkness of the wick, the haze of light surrounding the whole candle, now close the eyes and look into the third eye try to recapture the image, the colour if it draws away try and bring the image back into the centre.

Now open the eyes and try the exercise again, has anything changed is the light brighter, is there more than one aura, are you seeing a different shape, are you more immersed in the candle flame, is the colour of the flame changing, observe and release. Close the eyes and again rest in the centre of the forehead, repeat the exercise once more.

Let the eyes totally relax, check the body is still relaxed,

The candle is light, light however small, the candle flame gives off a light that can illuminate a room. If all you had was a candle to lighten the room, how you would treasure it, the candle is the difference between light and dark, fear and security, how this tiny flame can bring reassurance and comfort.

The Four Elements: Earth

Go into your usual relaxation routine.

Visualise a cord going from your root centre The Muladhara Chakra; down into the floor imagine it going into the ground, down through the rock, right down into the earth. Feel the warmth and the heat around the lower back,

Earth represents grounding, as in having your feet firmly on the ground. A firm connection to nature, her natural laws the continual ebb and flow and the circle of life. We visualise the colour red when working on the base charka.

The positive traits are stability, strength, survival, and power
The negative traits are fear, panic, disempowerment and weakness

Continue to feel yourself sinking into the floor, Feel your body on the mat, on the floor, the earth supporting you, and allow the body to let go, to let go imagine the body feeling solid, dense and heavy, persuade the body, encourage it, I am relaxing.
The floor is solid and strong, the earth is solid and strong it will support you, hold you, it is unable to let you go.
Feel the colour red spreading around your lower back, and draw upwards the strength, empowerment, stability, and courage.

The Affirmation is
I know no Fear

The Four Elements: Fire

Fire is associated with the Manipura Chakra at the belly a few inches above the navel it is the seat of emotions, including thoughts, judgement and opinions. Fire is also associated with going through the fire, cleansing, purification, therefore also connected with change, and in change transformation. We visualise the colour yellow when we work on the solar plexus, solar meaning sun or energy.

The positive traits are. Wholeness, tolerance, acceptance, growth, change, learning and progress.
The negative traits are. Intolerance, judgemental, continuing to make the same mistakes, staying stuck.

Take your attention to the solar plexus, be aware of the feeling of softness, the belly releasing, feel space, an empty chamber, as you breathe into this place imagine the breath as yellow golden mist, this golden mist streams into the belly, it swirls into the empty space, it flows around and fills your belly. It is now a golden ball of dense solid energy, a golden sun, a ball of light.

Now focus on the positive traits of yourself, draw in tolerance, acceptance of yourself and others, acknowledge that you are progressing and you have the ability to move through and beyond.

The Affirmation is
I am progressing

The Four Elements: Water

Water is associated with the lower abdomen the Svadishana Chakra, all liquids and bodily fluids are held in this centre. Water symbolises continual flow, movement, creativity, the ability to share emotions, open and friendly. When we work with the lower abdomen we visualise the colour orange. Water is continual movement and change, the ebb and flow, the coming and going, the ability to engage with life without feeling a victim when life doesn't go according to plan.

Positive traits. Confidence, considerate, friendly, sharing. Creative. Goes with the flow, and flexible.
Negative traits. Lack confidence, inconsiderate, unfriendly, cannot express feelings, not in harmony with life. Rigid and fixed

Take the attention to the abdomen and surround the whole of the area with a orange light, feel it flowing, moving, continuing to change direction, this colour orange brings joy, upliftment, and brightness.

Draw into yourself confidence, friendship, openness, be prepared to express yourself, be yourself, walk with a purpose, feel good about yourself. Hold these feelings for a few minutes.

The Affirmation is
I am Confident

The Four Elements: Air

Air is connected to the Heart Centre The Anahata Chakra. The emotions of love, harmony and peace, we feel in the heart, it is the bridge between the lower and higher Chakras. Here we fall in love, and trigger off all the other relative energies connected with love.

The chest is the organ for breathing we are looking towards openness to allow us to breathe mentally and physically. The prana is the life force, that vital energy that renews and gives us our spirit. When we focus on the heart centre we visualise the colour green, for harmony and balance.

Positive traits. We feel good about ourselves, we accept and tolerate, we are in love with life, we are human, we are sincere, and we try and have unconditional love towards others. We look for the good not the bad in others, we are positive. Negative traits. We cannot love ourselves, non acceptance, we find fault, we are insincere, and we cannot find the good in others. We are sometimes critical.

Take the attention to the heart centre, feel the rib cage spread and open, allow the expansion to fill the lungs, to widen and open, feel the space this expansion creates, surrender to those feelings of release, now visualise space, and in that space you are breathing in a fine green emerald mist, this swirls into the chest chamber, finding its way into corners, filling the chest centre with a fine green mist, feel it being absorbed, drenching the lungs with the colour green, and now the chest feels full, like a ball of emerald green light, it brings into your body calmness, balance, harmony and peace

The Affirmation is
I am Peaceful.

Postures with Attitude

Sometimes giving your postures a bit more flexibility and interest can enhance rather than dilute the practice. Too often we are looking for the perfect shape without any individuality, we stay rigid and breathe and forget about flow, postures are really moving meditation, and because we all have different bodies able and disabled we should be aiming for the essence of the posture not necessarily the perfect pose. I have called these postures with attitude, not because I want to change the status quo, rather to sometimes differ my approach to the word energy and chakras. If for any reason you are unable to practice Yoga at this moment in time, visualise yourself doing the work and thinking the positive attitude.

Attitude

Meaning: *Posture of body, behaviour, opinion, body language.*

Bhujangasana The Cobra

The cobra is of the Serpent family the snake, when aroused it can be dangerous, but generally can be quite harmless. The Cobra has a huge amount of strength especially when flexing and curving. The cobra demonstrates perfectly the attitude of strength arising in the body, the curving and twisting, the raising up off the ground shows flexibility. Forever on the alert he has a sharpness and quickness that enables him to strike. The open chest denotes freedom and space, the shoulders released bring the posture into your silent strength and alertness. The shedding of the skin and

moving on encourage you to change, and in change is transformation.

The Posture With Attitude

The concentration on the Vishuddhi chakra, symbol is the elephant, increases the strength of the Cobra posture. The attitude in the Cobra is this feeling of strength lying dormant in the base of the spine and slowly rising upwards as the posture unfolds, the flexibility that accompanies the movement together with the open chest allows freedom and space.

The slow deep raise gives you the sense of control and the deepening knowing of how you body is moving, the whole posture affirms I am strong. I am alert. I can move on.

Marjariasana The Cat

The Cat oozes sensuality, all felines prowl slowly and quietly, they can wait for their prey for hours on end, they have endless patience, but when they spring they are generally accurate. Observing a cat you will find her preening herself fastidiously, making use of her paws skilfully. The cat is extremely independent and can manage her own affairs. The cat is very flexible and well balanced, her nine lives confirm this. The cat that got the cream suggests smugness, we can interpret this as being kind to ourselves, nurturing, pampering.

your own sexuality, feel the sensual movements, feel the flexibility in your spine, honour your independence, keep moving with the flow, remembering the pause and the still point, when you think nothing is happening, that is when all is happening. Be kind to yourself, nurture yourself indulge. Allow yourself to loosen up mentally and physically.

Recognise and try to be in tune with your own natural body rhythms, keep trying to create harmony within the mind and body. Remembering like the cat Yoga is patience.

The Posture With Attitude

The wave like motion when performing the Cat mimics the inhalation and the exhalation, the rise and fall of the breath, the pause, and the still point. Move with the breath.
When the belly drops downwards and the buttocks spread, opening the lower back, you can actually feel the back speaking to you, the spine is in a vulnerable position, but the counter pose within the posture instantly rectifies this. The slow wave upon wave of drawing into the navel and releasing creates a harmony, a rhythm, which when the eyes are closed create the perfect moving meditation.

The attitude for this posture is own

Virabhadrasana The Warrior

The Warrior suggests strength he is in the same league as a Crusader, therefore he has to be full of energy, stamina and purpose, the need to have a voice as in walking your talk enhances the warriors position. In leadership he can manage with confidence, he has self control, good judgement, he is trustworthy and dependable courageous and honourable he can lead and be ready for the battle of life.

The Posture with Attitude

The warrior is not an easy posture because of the need for physical strength it is a weight bearing exercise. The sinking downwards increases the weight, and puts pressure on the knees and legs, the lifting and stretching upwards at the same time elongates the whole body. This posture affirms the attitude of strength, stamina, purpose, bravery, courage, walking your talk as in speaking up and honouring your capabilities. In this posture focus on these attitudes of mind, feel the empowerment of the posture. I am a Warrior.
Feel empowered. I am ready for life.

Balasana the Pose of the Child

The pose of the child is a posture in itself but is often used during the periods of relaxation. Here the child is folding into oneself coming back into the centre, we acknowledge the previous posture and reflect, we can now receive the tranquillity and stillness of this position. In this posture we are holding and nurturing. The curling up into the foetal position suggests we are coming back home. The child gives us that innocence, and simplicity to feel we can trust our inner self, we have no need to look outside, and all that we need is already here. I accept who I am.

The Posture with Attitude

Our attitude here is to seek within us the serenity, the calmness and reclaim for ourselves our worthiness. We are going back to a childhood posture with experience, strength and knowledge, we are not returning to innocence and vulnerability, in this posture we are celebrating our growth mentally and physically, and respecting ourselves for who we are. The pose of the child gives us the direct link to understand the essence of our postures, for it is in comparing the pose of the child with the warrior when we realise how the postures are speaking to us.

The Golden Orb

This Visualisation is done with a partner. Sit back to back with preferably someone of the same height, feel the base of the spine touch and the shoulders.

Connect to your partner and allow her back to support you, feel the base of the spine touching, the middle of the back, the shoulders touching. Allow the mind to draw away and start to focus on your partner's breathing, be aware of the sound, feel the movement, be aware of the pause, the still point. Can you feel the breath slowing? Take a deep breath and exhale with a sigh.

Now take your attention to your own breathing, how slow and even it feels. Are you sensing calmness, a slow even rhythm? Are you breathing in unison with your partner. Be aware of any sounds within your own body, any vibrations; allow the sound of your breathing, to take you deeper into relaxation.

Now be aware of the base of the spine and feel the warmth spreading around your lower back, moving around the middle of the back, spreading upwards bathing the shoulders in warmth and heat. You are beginning to feel a warm glow around your entire back, this energy is being transferred between the two of you. Stay connected with the breathing.

Now imagine a band of golden light spreading around your lower body, this huge band of gold expands outwards and enfolds you both.

When you are ready to take an in breath, draw up into your belly the band of gold,

feel it swirl into this area filling it with deep golden light, how strong the colour feels, as though your entire abdomen is full of gold, feel as though the belly is pulsating with energy.

When you are ready to take another breath, draw the band of gold into the heart chamber and feel the heart centre open to receive this golden light, feel the freedom, space, allowing you to breathe, I am where I need to be at this moment in time, any thoughts that may persist, acknowledge and let them go.

Be conscious of any feelings that may arise in the centre.

Now draw up the band of gold from the heart chamber into the shoulders around the neck and into the head. Feel the golden light moving, swirling, dissolving and melting any remaining tension

Now feel as though a golden spiral of golden light is moving freely up and down your spine, you are both entwined in a vortex of golden light, inside a golden orb, you feel so open and relaxed, so supported. Allow yourself to fully open into the experience.

Feel now the shoulders releasing forward, the neck and the chin to slightly drop, the belly to totally release from the experience, the whole body feels completely relaxed.

Take a few minutes to bring yourself out of the visualisation.

Stay for a while and share with your partner.

The Angel at your shoulder

Follow the usual relaxation technique before you begin the visualisation.

When we think of angels we imagine cherubs, angelic beings, and friends of light who are always around but need to be asked to come into our space. They like to be invited, but like any good friend if we trust them, they will come uninvited, they can come instantly when you call, at the speed of light because that is what they are.

Imagine around you light, surround yourself in a aura of white light, pure white light, feel it enclosing you, protecting you, feel light, feel free, visualise what a angel would look like, maybe a small angelic cherub with tiny wings, playful and mischievous or a stately angel a learned presence, if you had a Angel to call on what would she be, male or female, what would be their name, how would she be dressed, what is the size of her wingspan.

What a blessing it could be to have instant access to an angel friend. Ask the Universe now if you can have an Angel friend, give her a name and keep that name to yourself, you need do no more than that, you have already made the connection.

Now invite that named Angel friend to be part of your life here on earth, to feel close to you, feel the wings enfold you in a safe embrace, you can feel the softness, the closeness, when an Angel draws near, the peace that settles in your heart and moves around your aura is almost tangible it forms an instant mantle of protection.

Angels stay until the need is over. However, you do not always need to be in need to remember the Angels, tune into them, they are only a thought away.

Angels bring peace, harmony, worthiness, grace, strength, calmness, compassion, serenity,

Next time you pass a feather, an Angel has been near to you and left a calling card, remember to thank your Angel and to apologise for being out.

A Healing Visualisation

Lie in a comfortable position and go through the Yoga Nidra relaxing and releasing all the body. This may be difficult to do if thoughts of distress and anxiety are flooding into the mind. Try for a while to disconnect yourself from any anguish that maybe unbalancing the body at this moment in time, remember all the anxiety does not improve your situation, the negative thoughts are real and set up barriers to healing.

You are at this moment in a safe place, where with help, you can tune into a higher source of healing, allow yourself to surrender and let go of these emotions, you are wise enough to know you can change your thought patterns. Slowly give a command, a positive statement, I am relaxing, I am letting go of these feelings, I am giving myself up to a higher source, all is well.

As you begin to release this negative energy, you begin to feel a bit lighter. You start to relax, to give in to holding this condition to yourself. Already you are sharing this which you are holding, give yourself a few moments to allow this to happen.

Very calmly and assured bring into your mind the problem you are facing. In a positive voice to yourself, acknowledge the condition, I realise I have this condition which needs to be faced; I ask a higher source for help and guidance. Visualise your condition, mental or physical and isolate it, think only of the area in need of healing

Visualise a beam of deep blue light going directly to the area, surrounding it, enclosing, absorbing, feel the blue light working on that area, dissolving, cleansing, releasing your own healing energy, feel as though blue light is flooding through the blockage, and creating a return to positive energy, the blue healing light will loosen, feel that loosening, the blue healing light will soften, feel that softness, the blue healing light will encourage life-force, feel that life-force, the blue healing light is nourishing, feel that nourishment.

You now feel safe and secure because you know, this blue healing light is a direct link to that Universal source, that which is, and always will be, a part of your very existence.

Now visualise that area becoming healed, healthy, returning to normal, the affirmation is, I am healthy, repeat this affirmation to yourself inwardly in a clear strong voice, I am healthy, know that this healing experience will give you courage, strength to go forward and promote your growth and from growth to transformation.

Beachcombing

Use you usual relaxation technique to relax the body, feel warm, comfortable, and at ease.

Imagine yourself approaching a long sandy beach, the day is fine, warm and sunny, you look around and see you are completely alone, you have with you a small red velvet bag tied with a drawstring, this is to collect five special pebbles.

The only sounds are the waves gently lapping against the shingle on the sea shore, the waves go in and out with perfect timing, slowly and deliberately, you can take your shoes off and feel the warm grains of sand touch your feet, the softness, how the sand moulds to your feet, supporting you, feel yourself sinking into the sand. You move towards the water's edge, now you begin to feel the coolness on your feet, the damp solid sand, the firmness, you are aware of the footprints in the sand, solid footprints you are leaving behind, a seagull walks towards you, looking for food, he is picking over the trail of flotsam and debris left by the receding tide, dried up seaweed, sticks, bits of rope, shells, driftwood, feathers and pebbles.

The sun is warm on your face, and you are feeling good today, how precious life is, how privileged you are, walking on this quiet empty beach on such a wonderful day.

You have the small red velvet bag, you are looking for five pebbles of the same size, different colours, unusual shapes, pebbles that feel good in your hand that you feel drawn to

Look around you and see all the different pebbles and stones, some are misshapen, they are chipped with stormy seas, some have holes inside where maybe a creature once lived, some have seaweed anchored to them, some have lost their colour, you pick up a small black pebble, mottled with grey, hold it in your hand, it feels cool and comfortable, you feel drawn to this pebble so place it inside the red velvet bag.

As the wave recedes you notice a bright russet pebble rolling away with the shingle, it stands out so brightly, you stoop to pick it up and as you do your eye catches something shining in the sand, something bright and silvery, reach forward and pick it up, a pebble so shiny, so silvery, it almost looks like a small silver egg, it feels solid, hard and dense, it is the most beautiful pebble you have ever seen, how it glistens in the sunlight, it feels like a pearl in your hand, you feel drawn to this pebble so you place it in the red velvet bag .

The tide is still receding and you approach some small rock pools, they are clean and clear, full of life, jellyfish cling to the sides of the rocks, limpets hang on tightly, small crabs crawl under rocks as they see you looking into the pool, whelks move around with their heads outside their shells, a starfish is curled up against the rock, you stop for a moment and pause, you can hear the sound of the seashore, the movement of thousands of tiny animals, the seaweed, the whelks, it is a huge universal shifting vibration, the movement of life, look into the bottom of the pond and you see another pebble this one is blue, deep blue like Lapis Lazuli, it is speckled with pale blue and has a tiny hole in the centre, how strange a perfect circle right through the centre, you feel drawn to this pebble so you place it in your red velvet bag and walk on.

Ahead of you are sand dunes, they seem to go around the headland, they are high and deep covered in grasses and gorses, you intend to rest a while and as you approach you see an old coble lying on its side, it must have been left long ago because most of the timber is missing, the paintwork is flaking, and an oar lies broken on the floor, dried out seaweed and bits of rope lie over a seat, on the other seat is a warm blanket and a pillow the boat looks so inviting that you decide to lie down for a while, you step inside the boat and as you rearrange the blanket, you see inside a small black shiny pebble, this shiny pebble is jet black, smooth and bright, you hold it in your hand, you feel drawn to this pebble so you place it in your red velvet bag.

You now lie down, how good it feels to have the time to relax, you are safe, all you can hear is the gentle rush of the outgoing tide as it moves in and out, in and out against the seashore, you feel yourself drifting, melting, going with the flow of the tide, you are drawing in towards you and breathing in, the rhythm of the sea, the flow, the pause, the continual ebb and flow.

Autumn Days

Prepare for Visualisation by completing your relaxation technique.

The long summer days are slowly melting away, and we can feel the coolness in the air, Season of mellow fruitfulness, the last fruits of Summer, the Blackberry prepares us for change, The leaves are changing colour, the flowers beginning to fade, all around we are beginning to see a slowing down, a completion, the end of a cycle as a new part of the circle begins. The days seem to have a pause, stillness, a mature quality, a new shape to our day. The evening is coming earlier, there is a shadow creeping over the sun, bringing darker days, the time for preparation, the hibernation of the animals, the digging in to make a warm comfortable home, a time for reflection on those glorious days of Summer.

Every season has beauty and so has autumn, the gathering in of the harvest, indicates all is well. Now on this quiet autumn day we are in a garden, we have been given a large bag of daffodil bulbs to plant. There must be at least 50 bulbs, but it is a wonderful bright autumn day, very still, very quiet, and you are alone, alone with your own thoughts.

Open the bag and spread the bulbs on the path, you see the picture on the bag, it shows a golden display of bright yellow trumpets, and you wonder how this can manifest from what is in front on you, these daffodil bulbs, look at the shape, feel the texture in your hand, are they rough or smooth, the skins come off in your hands, they are dry and dusty, see the different sizes, some are large, some are small, some egg shaped, some like a small cone, they are presently asleep, but all will have within them a spark of life, a energy within the core of this bulb, a life-force that will urge growth, they will awaken but not yet.

Beside you are a trowel, plant pots, a watering can and a bag of earth. Take in your hand now a handful of earth and feel the energy that will nurture, feed, and allow growth. Allow this earth to trickle through your fingers sifting out any lumps or little stones, feel the lightness and allow the prana to enrich, allowing the earth to breathe, you are allowing yourself to be in the moment with nature, the bulbs are depending on you to get the planting right.

Now you fill the plant pot half full and place four bulbs inside, make sure they are upright, and of the same size, slowly sift the earth on top until they are covered, pat slightly down. The bulbs safely in the earth now are asking, pleading for that energy source that will begin growth.

Water, you take the watering can and slowly allow the trickle of water to gently soak into the earth, a long good drink, you can almost hear the sigh, as you visualise the bulbs drawing in the water through their skins they are now being nourished, fed, energised, they have started to awaken. When you have filled all the pots take them to a quiet spot, and sit for a moment.

Visualise now a bright Spring morning you have been watching these daffodils for some months now, they first appeared in the snow as shoots, bright green pushing up through the frosted pots, tall stalks, leaves, the flower buds forming, the swelling of the buds and then today flowers, huge golden trumpets, some are just about to burst through, some are fully open but they are all tall, straight, and healthy and you wonder how this could be so, when you remember the golden Autumn day when you first planted them. Take in that golden energy, and allow it to soak into you.

The Seasons speak to us of rebirth, renewal, the circle of life, and Nature at her finest hour.

Your Secret Glen

Prepare for Visualisation in your own way.

Imagine yourself setting out on a walk through the woods. You are alone, the day is bright and sunny and you have plenty of time to enjoy the day. You have been this way many times before and you know the path. It is an easy walk through an ancient wood, there are many varieties of trees, some huge old oaks, silver birch, sycamore, and some new saplings, the ground under your feet is dry and comfortable to walk on.

All around are ferns, wild garlic, herbs, and gorse. The odd rustle in the undergrowth indicates wildlife, and you see a squirrel scampering up a tree. You stop for a while watching and listening hoping to see the squirrel but it is too shy to come back out.

Soon the path takes you to a sunny area and you hear the sound of running water, as you approach you are aware of being in some small enclosure, a circular area, a miniature glen.

You have never noticed this place before, the small rocks are hiding a small tumbling waterfall, which gently cascades into a small deep pond, you look around, all is still, you are secluded from sight, there is a magical feeling, as though this miniature glen is not of the woods, it has a hidden secret, and you feel drawn towards the pond.

All around you birds are singing, butterflies are hovering, and the grass around the edge of the pond is dry and green and invites you to sit down, feel as though you are being led.

The tiny waterfall tumbles into the pond, but the pond itself is still, tiny water Iris and water lilies lie on the surface, small rocks are covered in moss, miniature ferns reach out to dappled places, small clumps of mini bulrushes surround the pond, the whole tiny glen is perfect.

You sit for a while, and watch the still pond, the hovering insects, a ripple, the sound of tumbling water, the continual movement, the occasional change of sound, the sound of the universe, the humming, the sound of O.M. the universal sound of the Earth, and within this sound you are still, you are embraced, you are at peace, you are in touch with the essence of your being. The sound of O.M. takes you deep inside yourself, the vibration sets up a Mantra and you feel yourself going deep within.

You open your eyes and look into the clear deep turquoise water, the pond is as clear as a mirror, in that mirror you now see your reflection. How well you look, how clear your complexion, how bright your eyes, how your hair shines in the sunlight, look deeper, and see the glow of your face, how the sun has touched your cheeks, how soft, relaxed and at ease it looks. Look deeper and allow yourself to merge into your reflection

You begin to feel a gentle presence around your shoulders, as though you are being held by gossamer wings, so fragile, so light, Ethereal.

Hold that feeling, stay a while, when you feel ready, slowly blink your eyes, and in cupped hands take a scoopful of water and gently bathe your eyes, feel the coolness, the pure mountain water cleansing, removing any tiredness, any weakness, any impurities. Allow this water to flow over your face and to awaken you. You now feel completely refreshed, relaxed, and renewed.

Rainbows

Go through your usual relaxation and feel the body relaxing, feel yourself sinking into the floor, completely letting go. Allow the shoulders to widen, the back to release, the buttocks to spread and allow the earth to support you, you are safe and well. Feel the breath coming and going slowing down with quiet, even rhythm. You feel comfortable, at ease, content, feel the space in the chest, the heart centre opening out, Breathe, Breathe. Connect with your calm centre and be fully in the moment.

You may start to be aware of feelings, feelings that you may not have felt for some time, feelings that are new to you, whatever feelings you are now experiencing allow them to be, witness them, let them come and go, try not to get into any dialogue with them.

Visualise now a rainbow over your body, a arc of pastel colour, it stretches right across your body, in this rainbow you can see, pink, lavender, golden yellow, pale blue, pastel green. The colours merge into each other. They have no definite beginning or ending. These colours are so calming, so healing, and so gentle, as you look at the rainbow you imagine how nice it would feel to just drift through a colour, to merge, to become absorbed in that colour.

Imagine walking through the colour lavender, walking through fields of French Lavender, rows and rows of lavender, endless rows, the light mauve has turned to deep purple. The breeze sways and the heady perfume fills the air, the flowers are all fully open, and the insects are in abundance. Visualise how the lavender is gathered, imagine the perfume when it is harvested, visualise it tied up in bunches like small sheaves of corn, small bags to hang by your bedside, essential oils, huge vats of lavender oil. Breathe, you can almost sense it. Breathe, feel the calmness. Breathe, feel the relaxation, surround yourself in the colour lavender.

Feel yourself melting and drifting back into the rainbow, see the rainbow surrounding your body and look at the golden yellow, how it seems to vibrate with energy.

Feel drawn towards the shade of gold and merge and melt into the vibrant colour gold, and you find yourself walking through a field of golden corn, see how the golden field sways in the breeze, the tall upright stalks looking up towards the sunshine, the bright golden ears, how intricate they are, the rustle as the whole field moves as one, visualise the harvest, the dust and separation of the ears, the sheaves of corn, the bales. All is safely gathered in, all is well. You are now feeling that golden energy, that upliftment, you feel free, calm and relaxed.

Feel yourself drifting back into the rainbow, the arc of colour surrounds your body, and you feel yourself drifting and melting into the colour green, a soft pale green, a gentle green, bringing balance, harmony, peace, filling you with healing, caressing you, nurturing you, I am where I am at this moment in time. All is well, and all is well.

The Monastery Garden

Prepare for Relaxation in your usual way.

Take your imagination to a place far away deep into the fells. You come across a Monastery. It is remote and secluded, time has not been kind, it stands weather beaten and uncared for, and no one has remained in this bleak position on the moors for many years. You sit on the grassy bank and look at the neglect and dereliction of this once fine place.

In places the roof has blown away, windows are missing and doors creak as they blow unbolted in the wind. The grass is growing out of the walls, birds have made nests in the hollows, swallows are in the eaves, old mill stones and wheels remain upturned, a rusty bucket remains tied to the well, the paths are uncared for, the bell has not been rung for many years now, the cloisters are empty, weeds push out of the arches that once housed silent monks, the courtyard is empty, no animals, no carts only a sad eerie silence.

The gardens are overgrown, the herbs and medicine plants no longer collected, and the building that once was thriving with medicinal herbs, potions and lotions is now still and quiet, only the empty jars and bottles remain on the wooden bench, dried faded flowers still lie on the windowsill their perfume long gone, dried and withered, faded into time, along with all who were here in a bygone age, you close your eyes and visualise what it may have looked like many years ago, and suddenly you are aware of the sound of horses hooves, of dray horses pulling up in the courtyard, their carts are full of hay, fodder for the animals is being taken away for winter, hens are clucking, a monk is feeding the livestock, whilst another collects the eggs, is that a quiet humming noise in the background almost like the sound of o.m. and do you hear the gentle chanting of monks.

The Monastery is big and fine, the cobbles and paths are well swept, all is tended, the place is alive, and everyone knows their labours. Inside the kitchen, a large fire is blazing with a kettle boiling on the hob, the pantry door is open and you are able to see all the produce gathered from the garden, jams, pickles, bottled fruits, wines, you can even smell the delicious aroma of newly cooked bread.

Your eye wanders to the walled garden and you open the wooden door to see silent monks at their labours, the garden is divided into three, flowers, vegetables and herbs, down the rows the monks are working in quiet meditation, the rows of vegetables are straight and even, the produce looks healthy, runner beans climb wigwams their bright orange flowers attracting the butterflies, old cottage garden flowers take up another patch, where a monk is gathering roses for the sick rooms.

The herb garden is minded by a monk whose fresh brown face shines out towards you, he smiles cheerfully and beckons you over, and as you move among the flowers and herbs you disturb the smell of camomile, apple mint, basil, and lavender. The fragrance fills the air.

You are now able to see into the Herbal kitchen, many different jars house the juices of herbs, seeds, and leaves are hanging in bunches, there are remedies made up on the wooden bench waiting to be taken to the sick room. There are jars of honey, pastes and ointments all labelled waiting to be collected.

The herbalist asks you if you are in need of any potions, or remedies, are you?

Could you do with a treatment, visualise yourself explaining your needs, either mental or physical, the herbalist listens, silently he takes down a jar and hands you a remedy you trust, and take the medicine, the herbs have a natural ability to heal, to soothe and to comfort, they will gently bring the balance back into your body.

Soon you are back in the silence, take time to come out of the visualisation. Take a few minutes to see if you were in the visualisation, did you receive, could you feel the Monastery coming once again to life.

Tibetan Journey To Meet Your Spiritual Guide.

Start the visualisation by settling into the relaxation position. Take this time to feel free to put aside and let go of any tensions, anxiety or worries. Give yourself the permission to be guided, remembering that nothing untoward can happen to you in relaxation, apart from the fact you will relax and feel at ease.

Concentrate for a few moments on your breathing and allow the breath to breathe the body, to take you down towards a quiet calm centre, a still point, a pause, a place where you feel free, where you are yourself, at one with yourself, alone and yet not alone. Feel as though you are waiting, waiting beside a long winding, twisting path, that leads up from the valley floor to a high mountain peak, on top of this mountain peak is a Tibetan Monastery. It seems as if it is in the clouds so high it is, you are in Tibet, The Kingdom In The Sky.

You have been invited to meet a spiritual master, so take this journey in quiet contemplation, with reverence, in stillness and solitude.

The peaks of the mountains are covered in snow, but it is warm in the valley. You slowly start the walk upwards, be aware now of how the body feels, allow yourself now to open out the heart centre, to feel open to any opportunities that may arise on the journey. Stay alert at all times, be aware of any feelings that may arise, instincts, thoughts, feel as though you are being helped up the mountain path for it is steep, stony and rugged in places.
A silence now surrounds you, solitude, and a peace that you may not have experienced for a long time.

The path winds up towards the snow covered peaks, and you are greeted on the way by a group of saffron robed monks, they are walking towards you in silence and quiet contemplation, this is walking meditation, but they still give you a blessing.

You now feel the thinness in the air as you climb higher and higher, the beauty of the mountains is awesome, the high rugged peaks covered in snow, the animals clinging to the side of the high mountains, the sparse grassland, the wind whistling around the mountain gorge, the sheer beauty of the land, the rich spiritual presence which seems to weaken the hardship, the harshness, and the poverty.

You now pass habitations, Tea Houses, small villages, prayer flags fluttering in the breeze. You hear the sound of prayer wheels turning, gongs. The women you pass are dressed for cold weather in colourful bonnets, layers of clothing, woven shawls, heavy skin boots, all made by themselves to protect them from the elements, they are hardy folk.
The cold is a constant companion up here in the high mountains and the people have to be completely self sufficient in food, clothing, oil for the lamps, medicine and fodder for the animals.

On you go, and the silence surrounds you. Soon you approach a gentle tumbling stream, it cascades down from the glacier, cold clear and fresh it looks almost aquamarine in the sunlight. You stop to fill your water carrier and take a long drink, how clear you feel, how energised, how refreshed.

Take the stepping stones over the shallow stream and arrive in a meadow, the animals are grazing they have heavy bells around their necks, you listen to the different sounds of the bells as the animals move around, birds of prey fly over, you can almost hear their wings moving, such is the silence.

In the distance you see pilgrims, and as they approach they also give you a blessing. The way ahead is now clear, you can see the Monastery in the distance, smell the incense burning, the oil in the lamps, prayer flags are whipped around by the breeze, bells and gongs compete with each other, soft chanting fills the air. The courtyard is full of silent monks, pilgrims and visiting Spiritual leaders. Today you are allowed inside to meet the spiritual master, this wise one who awaits you.

It is a special day for you today. Allow yourself to be guided by a trainee monk, and sit on the soft velvet cushion in front of your guide. Take the attention to your breathing allowing the breath to breathe the body, feel deep inside the calm centre, the stillness, the silence, the solitude, I am. Feel

his calmness, peace, wisdom, his healing presence, his compassion. Allow yourself to blend with his spiritual presence, to completely surrender to the moment. Absorb all that is there with you, now.

That was a spiritual experience, you feel different. You are now given the opportunity to ask any questions, allow yourself a few moments to form a question or ask for guidance for any part of your life that may be in need. Whatever comes into your thoughts at this moment in time allow it to be transferred to your spiritual guide, you may not receive the answer at this moment in time but be prepared to wait, be assured he knows what you have requested. Let this problem or question now go, and allow it to be transformed. Receive now his blessing and healing. Take the attention back to the breath, feel how deep and even the breathing has become. How calm and healed you feel, how centred, and also feel the presence in your heart.

You now come out of the monastery into brilliant sunshine, you know you have been healed, you know because you feel so alive.

The Pipe of Peace

This is a particular good visualisation for anyone who has been unable to resolve personal disagreements, arguments or relationship problems. Sometimes we can let go of a situation and have peace in our lives without actually facing the person or situation involved if we visualise the negative problem going back to a Mother Earth. If we know we are up against a problem, however hard it feels, we can stand back and allow a higher source to try and dissolve and defuse the situation. Smoking the pipe of peace was a very sacred ritual for the American Indian; it was a spiritual wise event.

The pipe was connected to the elements of the earth and the four kingdoms. The creator breath is the common source of all that is. The pipe ceremony was a serious offering to the earth and all that is; The American Indian knew that nature impregnates all things, and that the earth and everything on it was precious. They loved more than anything the land. We can use the Peace Pipe as a symbolic gesture to allow all things negative to return to the earth and become transformed in the circle of life.

Smoking The Pipe of Peace.

Visualise the vast land that used to belong to American Indians, they were free to roam the prairies and hunt in the hills and mountains. The Earth was sacred to them, they never left a trail or mark upon the land, they took only what was necessary. Imagine you are sitting on the dry brown earth outside a large Indian Tippee. Many

peaceful Indians are gathering for the Smoking of the Peace Pipe Ceremony. You are in a circle, and dressed as an Indian Squaw/Brave, you belong here. The Indians are gathering on the ridge waiting for the chief to summon them down onto the flat land, many hundreds of Indians have been invited, the noise of the drums, the horses, the dancing and singing are creating a potent energy and power that seems to make you feel very strong and brave. You look to see the clothes you are wearing, a brown animal skin, moccasins of hide fastened with laces made of beads, you have ornaments and feathers in your hair, what colour is your hair, how tall are you, others are dressed the same, do you recognise anyone? Feel the warm brown sandy earth in your hands, your connection to the earth, to the four elements.

Now the Indians are coming down from the ridge. Look at the colours of the dress how each one differs from Brave to Chief, be aware of headdress, feathers, shoes, clothing, look at the beautiful horses how tame they are, how calm. Listen to the words the Indian whispers into the horses ears. The horses walk slowly into the compound. The Indians all gather around waiting for the ceremony to start.

The wise Indian Chief appears and sits on the dry earth beside you; he has in his hand the 2 pieces belonging to the sacred pipe the stem, and the bowl. You watch as he joins the sections together, they fit so neatly. Now he fills the bowl with the tobacco, lights the pipe and begins to meditate on the breath. He believes the smoke is symbolic of the circle of life, the ever changing circle of birth, death, return to the great spirit, and completion of the wheel.

The silence surrounds you as you wait for the pipe to be handed around the circle, allow your eyes to remain still and focused behind closed eyelids.

Any quest you may have can be transformed, the pipe of peace can allow you to apologise, to be forgiven, to resolve an issue, to heal any emotional wounds, to say sorry, you can do this now as the Indian Chief hands to you the Peace Pipe, feel it in your hands, the warmth of the bowl, the length of the stem, know that this ancient custom is going to work for you and bring you peace. Hand over to Mother Earth that which you no longer need to hold onto.

You feel safe, you are safe. Allow yourself to hand over freely, empower yourself with your own personal strength, you are affirming that strength now. Remain at ease, you have no need to struggle, it seems the Peace Pipe is aware of your needs, just allow this to happen.

You can feel your body soften, as you feel your heart open, as you feel your negative thoughts melt, as you give way to forgiveness.

I return to that great source of energy all that I no longer need.

Remain still, and feel as though a weight has been lifted, as you begin to return from the visualisation.

41

Magnolia Visualisation

Prepare yourself for relaxation. When the body is warm, comfortable and at ease, take a few deep breaths and feel yourself sinking down into the floor, feel the weight in the body releasing, and as you release, feel as though the entire body is spreading, widening, relaxing and melting away any tension, until you feel a softness, a stillness move through you. Stay with the breath and just witness the coming and going of the breath as the body moves to the rhythm. Feel the breath slow the body down, drifting down into your calm centre.

Visualise yourself standing at the top of a flight of ten stairs, and as you walk down these stairs your body will become relaxed and at ease.

The stairs are carpeted in deep indigo blue and the walls are pale blue, as your bare feet touch the carpet you can feel the softness, the comfort, the support.

As you descend the first stair repeat to yourself, I am supported, as you descend the second and third stair, repeat to yourself I am at ease, at the fourth stair you are beginning to feel heavy, allow the stairs to support you, the fifth and sixth stair and you are beginning to feel as though the body is just drifting downwards.
At the seventh stair you can see the end to the staircase, now at the eighth stair you can see a heavy wooden door.

On descending the final two stairs you are able to see the door is slightly ajar, and you have permission to go through this door. Turn the wooden handle and go through the door.

Stepping through the door you find yourself in a walled secret garden, the flower beds are full of cottage garden flowers, it is May time, bees and butterflies are gently hovering, in the centre of the lawn is a old magnolia tree laden with blossom, it is a deep shade of pink some petals seem frilled, and seem tinged with red.

Underneath the tree, late daffodils, early tulips and bluebells are clumped together. You walk over to the tree and feel the cool spring grass underneath your feet, feel the connection to the earth, feel the prana being absorbed into the soles of your feet, the grass is new, fresh, alive, and you can almost feel the life force and energy.

You lie down against the old magnolia tree trunk and look up into the dappled sunlit branches, the warmth of the early sun warms your face. The heady perfume of the blossom which surrounds you, makes you feel heady and drowsy, you gaze into this large blossom which droops down from a low hanging branch.

It slowly starts to change shape into a giant blossom bell, and as you drift into a relaxed sleep you find yourself inside this bell with your head gently resting on a pillow of blossom.

How soft this feels, how safe and secure, how peaceful, you feel as though a mantle of light has been placed around you, holding you, bringing you back into that safe place where you want to be.

It may be some time since you felt so

peaceful, so relaxed, so cherished, so hold this feeling that is sweeping gently around your body, nurturing you, touching your heart.

Hold it for just a few moments until as you let it go, you are left with the delicate touch of what you have, and always will have within you. The ability to receive.

Global Peace

This is a Meditation for all those times when we feel helpless, when words are empty and we cannot express ourselves the tragedy is so overwhelming. What can we do about man's inhumanity to man, how can we find the middle way when there is so much greed, corruption, inequality and injustice, how do we help the innocent caught up in the middle of wars not of their making, how do you help someone to find their way in the darkness when you feel so troubled yourself.

This meditation came when we were all lost for words September 11th 2001. I could not believe such evil and hate existed, and the lengths man could go to, to destroy another's life. I could only pray for those lost persons and the families they had left behind under such a harrowing experience, and in the Yoga Class this is what we did.

This Meditation is for all those souls who are in need, suffering through no fault of their own, who are the victims of Terrorism, War, Oppression, Famine, Cruelty, Inequality and Captivity, who suffer because of man's inhumanity, ignorance, greed, and corruption.

Begin the Meditation by sitting in a circle. Light a Large Candle or many singles. Sit upright, feel comfortable and alert. Feel yourself relaxing and allow yourself to feel open, first of all feel as though you are surrounded by blue light, this Aura of light starts at the crown of the head and spreads completely around your body. As you breathe in and out, the Aura widens and deepens sending out a glow of blue that

merges with the person next to you, touching, connecting and uniting, the room is now a circle of blue light, visualise this blue light as peace and healing for the entire Planet. Allow the heart centre to open and feel compassion, tenderness and empathy.

Peace begins at home and in our own lives, think now of your family, each and every one, and send out a message of peace. Think of your extended family and send out thoughts of healing and peace. Think of your neighbours. Send out thoughts of peace even if you disagree with them. Remember your colleagues at work, even though you may not feel friendly with them, send out thoughts of healing and peace.

Now think of all your friends and acquaintances and especially people you do not get on with, send out thoughts of healing and peace.

Now think of all those places you have been to, countries you have visited, all over the world, people you know in far off lands, and send to them a message of healing and peace.

Now think of the Armed Forces we have in this country who fight for us to remain free, the young people and their families, who wait behind. Send out thoughts of healing and peace.

Visualise the Planet Earth and surround it in an aura of blue light. Allow that blue healing light to fill the planet with peace and healing, repeat to yourself, I send peace and healing to Planet Earth.

Visualise everyone and everything that lives on this planet. Send a beam of blue light and repeat to yourself, I send peace and healing to all mankind.

Send now Peace to the East, Peace to the West, Peace to the North, and Peace to the South.

I send peace to every corner of the world.

Imagine a flock of beautiful white doves flying high in the sky, taking your message around the world, and spreading the word,

Om shanti

The Crystal Cave

Follow your usual relaxation technique, breathing deeply and evenly, finding your calm centre and allowing the body to remain still, and at ease.

You are walking in the woods along a pathway on a warm summer day, the ground is damp underfoot from a recent summer shower, all around the birds are singing, the trees are glistening, you can smell the freshness in the air, the sun is shining through the trees and you are beginning to feel warm, you stop for a moment to look around, the path is winding and you are following the stream and beginning to climb, you have to watch your footsteps as you move over cobbles and tree roots, some stones may be slippery. You are aware of the sounds of the dripping rain from the tree branches, a rustle in the undergrowth, the sound of the tumbling stream which is now widening, the height of the trees, the shady area you are now approaching.

The climb becomes a little steeper here and you stop for a moment to see a small bridge ahead of you, from here the water is tumbling over large rocks forming pools, and a small weir, you go over the bridge and join the path which leads upwards, you are out in the sunshine again, the light is so bright, so piercing that you almost need to shade your eyes, it just feels like one of those special summer days, when all is well.

Suddenly you hear the sound of rushing water and look up to see a waterfall cascading, the sunlight is shining directly on the flow creating a rainbow, all the colours of the spectrum sparkling in the sunlight, as you move further on you discover the path goes directly behind the waterfall, the path is wide, safe and dry, so you decide to explore further, as you walk slowly behind the waterfall you find yourself at the entrance to a crystal cave, the light from the waterfall and the sun has illuminated the cave into a wonderful cavern of light. The crystal is sparkling, glittering, the light is reflecting onto the back of the waterfall creating a dazzling display of colour, you stop and gaze at this wonderful happening, the sound of the cascading water is loud but you are unafraid, because you are safe and dry and the path is wide, all the colours of the rainbow present themselves in splendour you are dazzled by the beauty.

Every part of your body can now be energised, every chakra can be balanced, every cell in your body can be renewed with life force, with energy, and any negative ions can be transformed into positive. You are now refreshed, renewed, drenched in prana.

You can now walk slowly right out the other side and come back onto your path, what a experience to have walked behind a waterfall, what a discovery, what a secret place you have found, how exciting to feel that any time, any time at all you can come to this haven of peace and natural wonder and become recharged and rebalanced. All is well. I am well. The affirmation is, all is well.

The Alpine Lake

Begin your usual relaxation, be comfortable and warm, adjust the body until you feel completely at ease, feel yourself drifting and melting into the floor, you are still and at rest, allow the body and mind to remain restful as you go on a journey to your alpine lake.

You have a day to yourself to go on a long high walk up the mountains, you may feel like taking with you a partner or a companion, or go by yourself. You have in your rucksack, a flask, lunch and extra warm clothing for the journey takes you high into hills and the climate changes.

Be ready to set out, you are well prepared and the day is warm. You start to walk along the valley floor, the air is clear and fresh, and the ground is dry underfoot. You are able to see ahead of you the high mountains you will climb, they seem so far away and you wonder how you will ever make it.

Around you are Alpine meadows, the grass is kept short by the cows grazing, you hear the sound of bells ringing they are hanging around their necks, all different sizes and sounds. These Alpine cattle are a beautiful shade of brown, tawny brown, fawn,

beige, and cream a variety of shades, they seem so friendly and allow you to gently stroke them, how docile they are and curious.

The meadows are full of alpine flowers their heads lifted towards the sun, they peep out of stones and crevices, they hide behind rocks, they carpet the valley and the hills, they look so delicate and fragile, but they are strong and hardy. A stream of water runs over your path and you look up to see a cascading waterfall falling from the hillside, the water looks cold and icy.

The path seems to move upwards now and you are beginning to feel warm, the road ahead is steep and long and you can see snow covered peaks, high lofty Tors, craggy cliffs, and scree covered slopes, you know you are climbing higher, your breathing is more laboured and the backpack is beginning to feel heavy.

Soon you come to a stone bridge, the river is rushing through, emerald green, clear, and icy it comes from the glacier not far ahead, it gushes and teems over the rocks, creates spray, which catches the sunlight and shimmers with colour. Icy pools are full of beautiful coloured stones, ancient pebbles that have been brought down by falls of rock, avalanches, and weather, you walk over the bridge and then turn and look back at the scenery it is so very beautiful, so majestic, so dramatic, the path stretches way back you cannot believe how far you have travelled.

You are now in sight of a Alpine Hut a sanctuary, a safe haven for travellers, a place of rest, you approach the hut and find yourself a bench, it looks directly onto a glacier lake the imposing mountains behind are covered in snow, deep snow, you can see from your safe place gullies and ridges, the tops of the mountains are narrow and they jut up into the sky like lofty pinnacles

The glacier lake is pale green, with a smokey white denseness, pure glacier water; it is still, and deep. You stay and rest and give yourself some refreshments, although snow covered mountains surround you, the sun is warm on your face, your whole body feels warm, the sky is clear, the alpine air is fresh, take yourself some long deep breaths, and look towards the mountains, a pair of eagle circle, they are gliding, soaring high and now hovering, see the width of their wingspan, how the wings appear clipped at the edges, how they just fit into this landscape, dramatic and majestic, just like the mountains.

Now the time has come to go back down the mountain for you have travelled far, The path ahead is easy now you are slowly walking down towards the valley floor, you pass the stone bridge, the alpine meadows, the cattle in the field, some mountain goats clinging to the edges, and soon you see in the distance the small church spire, the alpine houses decked out with window boxes full of flowers, winter fuel stacked up against the walls, the tumbling stream crosses your path, and you find yourself back in the valley, what a wonderful experience, what a wonderful day you have had, a special day, a day to remember.